I0409333

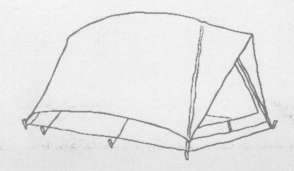

THE STORY
OF ME AND MY
DAD

First published by Exclusive Editions Publishing Ltd in 2013
LIFE CANVAS is an imprint of Exclusive Editions Publishing Ltd

Copyright © Exclusive Editions Publishing Ltd 2013

LIFE CANVAS and the accompanying logo are trademarks of
Exclusive Editions Publishing Ltd

Produced by Tall Tree Ltd
Illustrations by Apple Agency

All rights reserved. No part of this publication may be reproduced,
stored in a retrieval system or transmitted, in any form or by any means,
electronic, mechanical, photocopying, recording or otherwise, without the
prior permission of the copyright holder.

ISBN 978-1-4723-0738-5
GTIN 5060292800981

Printed in China

A LETTER TO DAD ABOUT THIS BOOK

Date ....

Dear Dad,

love from...

where ....

when ....

JUST THE
TWO OF US

OUR JOURNEY TOGETHER

IF YOU FOLLOW THIS THREAD
THROUGH THE BOOK, YOU'LL SEE
PHOTOS, SOME OLD AND SOME
NEW, SOME OF YOU, SOME OF ME
AND SOME OF US TOGETHER.

stick your photo here

ALL ABOUT MY DAD

Dad's favourite colour ....

Dad's dream car ....

Dad's favourite song ....

Dad's best friend ....

Dad's favourite TV show ....

Dad's dream holiday ....

Dad likes to eat ....

Dad likes to play ....

LOVE THE SONG OR HATE IT?

song	Dad does this when it's playing
1.	a b c
2.	a b c
3.	a b c
4.	a b c
5.	a b c

a. Dances like a crazy person b. Doesn't move from his chair c. Turns it off

DAD AND I LAUGHED
SO MUCH WHEN...

Dad likes to do these things...*

	really likes	likes	pretends to like	dislikes
Watching television	☐	☐	☐	☐
Going to work	☐	☐	☐	☐
Lying around	☐	☐	☐	☐
Cooking	☐	☐	☐	☐
Shopping online	☐	☐	☐	☐
Fixing things	☐	☐	☐	☐
Working out	☐	☐	☐	☐
Playing on a games console	☐	☐	☐	☐
Shopping with Mum	☐	☐	☐	☐
Mowing the lawn	☐	☐	☐	☐
Meeting friends	☐	☐	☐	☐
Watching sport	☐	☐	☐	☐
Playing games with me	☐	☐	☐	☐
Barbecuing	☐	☐	☐	☐
....	☐	☐	☐	☐
....	☐	☐	☐	☐
....	☐	☐	☐	☐
....	☐	☐	☐	☐

*Does he really?

stick your photo here

YOU ALWAYS SAY THIS

THINGS YOU'VE
TAUGHT ME

✓

How to throw a ball ☐
How to ride a bike ☐
How to light a barbecue ☐
How to cast a fishing rod ☐
How to tie my shoelaces ☐
How to make breakfast ☐
How to make my bed ☐

.... ☐

.... ☐

.... ☐

.... ☐

.... ☐

.... ☐

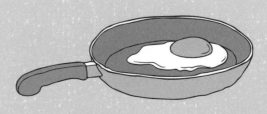

Remember when?

Use this space to write about something that happened to you and your Dad.

....
....
....
....
....
....
....
....
....
....
....
....
....
....
....
....

WHEN WE GO OUT **TO EAT DAD** ALWAYS ORDERS

Starter

Main

Dessert

Takeaways available • Service not included • Private parties catered for

stick your photo here

YOU EMBARRASSED ME WHEN...

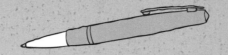

WHEN I DO THESE THINGS
IT MAKES YOU
MAD

1. ....
2. ....
3. ....
4. ....
5. ....

IF NO ONE TOLD YOU WHAT TO WEAR...

HATS

HAIR

TOPS

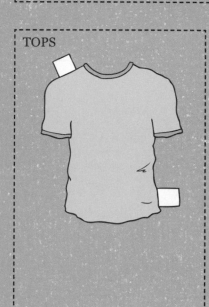

TROUSERS

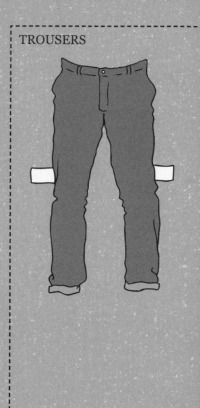

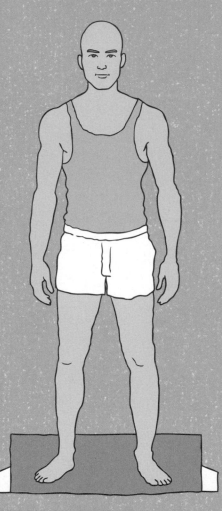

SHOES

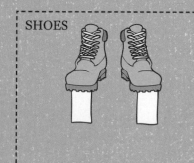

ACCESSORIES

YOU'D WEAR THIS!

List or draw your Dad's fashion failures!

MY FAVOURITE THINGS
TO DO WITH YOU

....

....

....

....

....

....

....

....

....

....

....

....

....

....

....

....

....

DAD'S FAVOURITE
GADGETS

Colour in the smile rating.

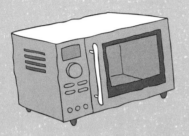

Dad's rating

Remote control 😄 🙂 😐 ☹️ 😦

Mobile phone 😄 🙂 😐 ☹️ 😦

Microwave 😄 🙂 😐 ☹️ 😦

Power drill 😄 🙂 😐 ☹️ 😦

E-reader 😄 🙂 😐 ☹️ 😦

Television 😄 🙂 😐 ☹️ 😦

Computer 😄 🙂 😐 ☹️ 😦

GPS 😄 🙂 😐 ☹️ 😦

MP3 player 😄 🙂 😐 ☹️ 😦

Camera 😄 🙂 😐 ☹️ 😦

Games console 😄 🙂 😐 ☹️ 😦

 😄 🙂 😐 ☹️ 😦

Stick in your favourite photo of you and your Dad doing one of your favourite things.

You like to watch these TV programmes...

but do I?

	really likes	likes	pretends to like	dislikes
	☐	☐	☐	☐
	☐	☐	☐	☐
	☐	☐	☐	☐
	☐	☐	☐	☐

I like to watch these TV programmes...

but do you?

	really likes	likes	pretends to like	dislikes
	☐	☐	☐	☐
	☐	☐	☐	☐
	☐	☐	☐	☐
	☐	☐	☐	☐

Kind   Understanding   Thoughtful

Generous   Playful

A BICYCLE WHEEL OF YOUR CHARACTER!

Happy

Silly   Charming

Colour in the wheel to match your Dad's personality. Use these
words as a guide, but pick some of your own. The bigger the
wedge, the more like that he is.

Dad's best jokes

....
....
....
....
....
....
....
....

Dad's worst jokes

....
....
....
....
....
....
....
....

stick your photo here

MY DAD'S THE BEST BECAUSE...

....
....
....
....
....
....
....
....

1st

SAY IT WITH PICTURES

Say it with pictures instead of words and see if Dad knows what you're saying!

Dad's best advice

....

....

....

....

....

....

....

stick your photo here

DAD FIXED
THESE THINGS

1. ....
2. ....
3. ....
4. ....
5. ....

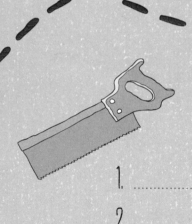

BUT COULDN'T
FIX THESE

1. ....
2. ....
3. ....
4. ....
5. ....

Things Dad Dislikes

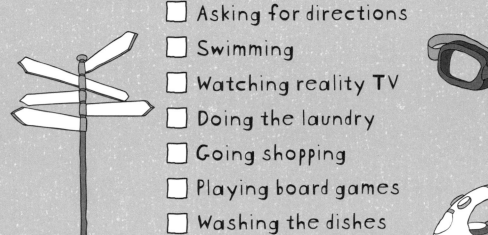

- [ ] Asking for directions
- [ ] Swimming
- [ ] Watching reality TV
- [ ] Doing the laundry
- [ ] Going shopping
- [ ] Playing board games
- [ ] Washing the dishes
- [ ] Driving me around

- [ ] ....
- [ ] ....
- [ ] ....

I'M SORRY

THE JUDGING PANEL
GAVE YOU THESE
MARKS OUT OF 10

Dress sense

Creativity

Craziness

Patience

Music you listen to

Silliness

Thoughtfulness

Generosity

Mark Dad from 0–10 on the judges' paddles.

IF EVERY DAY WAS FATHER'S DAY WE WOULD

....
....
....
....
....
....
....
....

YOU MAKE ME ANGRY WHEN...

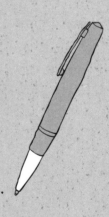

....
....
....
....
....
....

where ....

when ....

I WISH I'D TAKEN
A PICTURE WHEN

Draw the missed photo opportunity in the frame below.

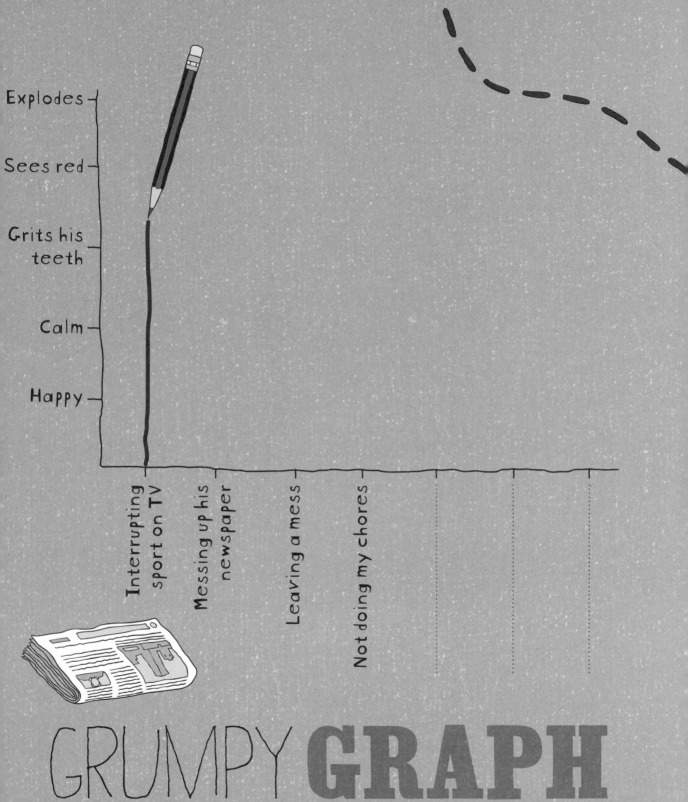

Explodes —

Sees red —

Grits his
teeth —

Calm —

Happy —

Interrupting
sport on TV

Messing up his
newspaper

Leaving a mess

Not doing my chores

GRUMPY GRAPH

Complete this line graph to see how grumpy Dad is.

CAUGHT ON CAMERA

Dad not looking his best

where ....

when ....

PLEASE DON'T EVER DANCE TO
THESE SONGS IN PUBLIC...

1. ....
2. ....
3. ....
4. ....
5. ....

...AND DON'T SING
THESE SONGS
OUT LOUD EITHER!

1. ....
2. ....
3. ....
4. ....
5. ....

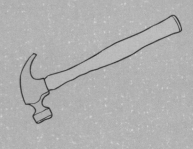

Rating Dad's skills

Circle the face that best shows how good your Dad is at...

Fixing things ☹ 😐 ☺   Listening ☹ 😐 ☺

Singing ☹ 😐 ☺   Telling stories ☹ 😐 ☺

Dancing ☹ 😐 ☺   Playing sport ☹ 😐 ☺

Cleaning ☹ 😐 ☺   .... ☹ 😐 ☺

Telling jokes ☹ 😐 ☺   .... ☹ 😐 ☺

Driving ☹ 😐 ☺   .... ☹ 😐 ☺

Cooking ☹ 😐 ☺   .... ☹ 😐 ☺

Giving hugs ☹ 😐 ☺   .... ☹ 😐 ☺

- [ ] Play a board game
- [ ] Wash your car
- [ ] Go to the beach
- [ ] Watch a match
- [ ] Go on an outdoor adventure
- [ ] Have a barbecue
- [ ] Play a game of football
- [ ] Ride our bikes
- [ ] ....
- [ ] ....
- [ ] ....
- [ ] ....

WHAT SHOULD WE DO TOGETHER?

stick your photo here

our best
F MIL HOLI   .

1. ....
2. ....
3. ....
4. ....
5. ....

DAD'S HEROES!

List the top five people your
Dad admires most.

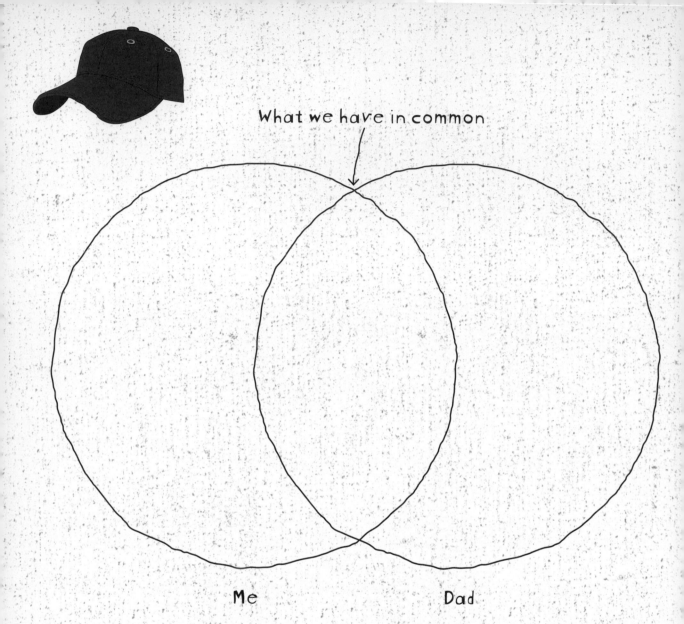

What we have in common

Me   Dad

I'M JUST LIKE YOU!

WE NEARLY GOT INTO TROUBLE
WITH MUM WHEN WE...

....
....
....
....
....
....
....
....

stick your photo here

MY FAVOURITE
ADVENTURE WITH YOU

things to do
ON A RAINY DAY

I promise to...

1. ....
....

2. ....
....

3. ....
....

4. ....
....

5. ....
....

LAUGH-O-METER

Complete this bar chart to see how funny Dad is at...

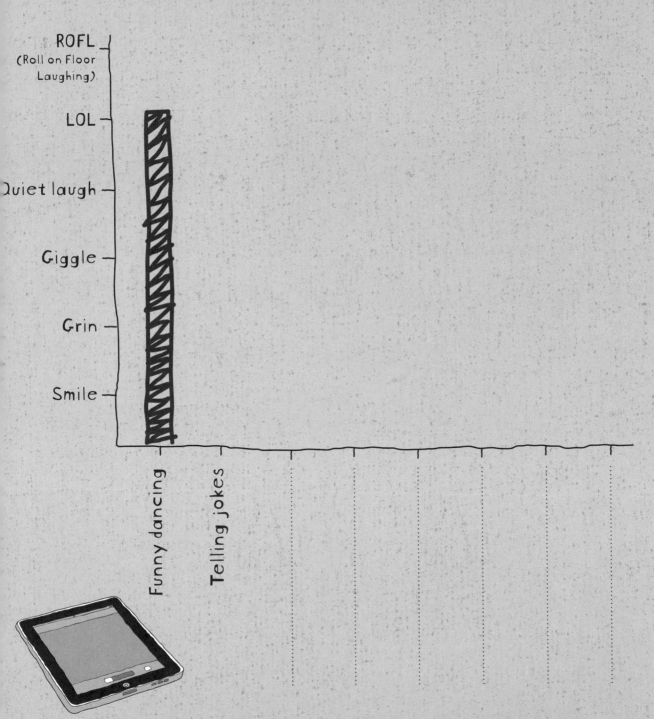

WE MUST DO
these things together

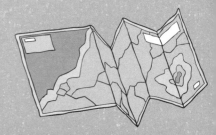

WHY YOU MEAN THE WORLD TO ME

THIS IS US NOW